HANDS-ON LETTERS
Cut-ups

by Marilynn G. Barr

Publisher: Roberta Suid
Production: Little Acorn & Associates, Inc.

CUT-UPS
Entire contents copyright © 2004
by Monday Morning Books, Inc.

For a complete catalog, write to the address below:
Monday Morning Books, Inc.
PO Box 1134
Inverness, CA 94937

Call our toll-free number: 1-800-255-6049
E-mail us at: MMBooks@aol.com
Visit our Web site:
http://www.mondaymorningbooks.com

ISBN 1-57612-194-1

Printed in the United States of America
9 8 7 6 5 4 3

Contents

Introduction

Cut-ups includes alphabet lacing cards, letter cards, and a variety of project ideas for creative skills practice fun. There are two lacing card patterns for each letter of the alphabet and a set of upper- and lower-case letter cards. Vowel patterns include one each for a short and long vowel. Lacing card patterns are designed for children to color, cut out, punch holes and lace with yarn or string as they learn alphabet skills. A diagram of the assembled lacing card is also included on each pattern page. Children will learn to recognize and match alphabet pictures and letters and develop fine motor skills. Additional Cut-ups activities can be found on pages 62-63.

Prepare a workstation stocked with lacing card patterns and a variety of craft materials for lots of creative skills practice fun. Use baskets or plastic see-through containers to organize the workstation. Store small items in separate plastic resealable bags. Use the Cut-ups Supplies Checklist on page 7 to take inventory of supplies on-hand and needed supplies. Reproduce the Request For Craft Supplies form on page 64 for children to take home asking parents to help stock your workstation.

Cut-ups Lacing Cards

Reproduce sturdy lacing card patterns from card stock, oak tag, or poster board. Glueless wallpaper, felt, and laminated paper also make sturdy materials for lacing cards.

Materials:

Cut-ups patterns	scissors	crayons or markers
Letter Cards	hole punch	yarn
twist ties		

Reproduce a Cut-ups pattern for each child to color. Write the corresponding upper- and lower-case letters on the front of each child's pattern. Or, reproduce and cut apart the corresponding letter cards for each child to glue onto each of the Cut-ups. Help each child cut out and punch holes around his or her pattern to form a lacing card. Show how to thread yarn through a twist-tie needle (p. 6). Demonstrate how to straight or loop lace yarn through the holes around a lacing card as shown on pages 6 and 7. Help children make and thread twist-tie needles and lace cards. Then help children tie the loose ends of yarn together.

Poster-sized Lacing Cards

Make poster-sized lacing cards for display or to hang from the ceiling.

Materials:

Cut-ups patterns	poster- or corrugated board	scissors
crayons or markers	hole punch	yarn
glue		

Enlarge and transfer Cut-ups patterns and letter cards (p. 60-61) onto poster or corrugated board. Color, cut out, and punch holes around each Cut-up to form a lacing card. Lace thick yarn through the holes in each pattern, then tie the loose ends of yarn together. Glue a matching upper and lower-case letter card onto the lacing card. Mount the finished lacing cards on a display board or measure, cut, and tie a length of yarn to the top of each lacing card to hang from the ceiling

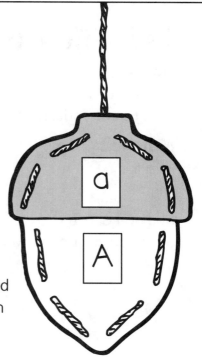

My Alphabet Cut-ups Portfolio

Provide children with materials to make portfolios to store and carry Cut-ups patterns.

Materials:

heavy construction paper	crayons or markers	hole punch
yarn	stapler	Cut-ups patterns
oak tag	scissors	resealable plastic bag

Provide each child with a large sheet of heavy construction paper. Have children fold construction paper to form a portfolio (diagram A). Encourage children to use crayons or markers to decorate the outside of their portfolios. Help each child punch two holes along the top of his or her portfolio (diagram B). Measure, cut, and tie a length of yarn through each set of holes to form portfolio handles.

Reproduce oak tag Cut-ups patterns for each child to color and cut out. Help each child punch holes around his or her Cut-ups pattern to form a lacing card. Provide each child with a resealable plastic bag filled with assorted lengths of yarn for lacing cards. Have children store their Cut-ups lacing cards and bags of yarn inside their portfolios.

Twist-Tie Needles

Provide children with twist ties to make
sewing needles for lacing Cut-ups
lacing cards and other sewing practice projects.

Materials:

twist ties

yarn

Fold over and form a loop with one end of a twist tie. Twist
and wrap to form a sewing needle eye. Then lace yarn through
the eye.

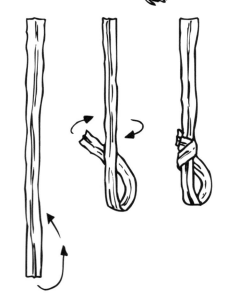

Straight Lacing Directions

Reproduce and enlarge this chart for children to practice straight lacing skills.
Color, cut out, laminate, and display the chart in an alphabet practice workstation.

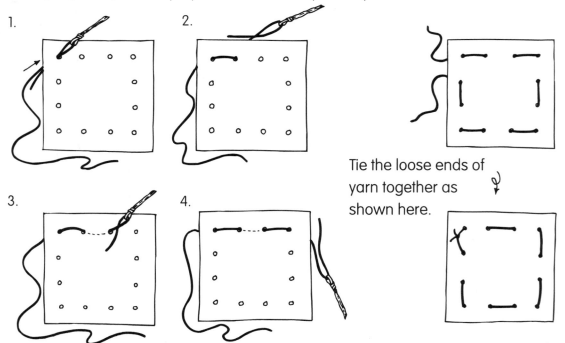

1.

2.

3.

4.

Tie the loose ends of
yarn together as
shown here.

Loop Lacing Directions

Reproduce and enlarge this chart for children to practice loop lacing skills.
Color, cut out, laminate, and display the chart in an alphabet practice workstation.

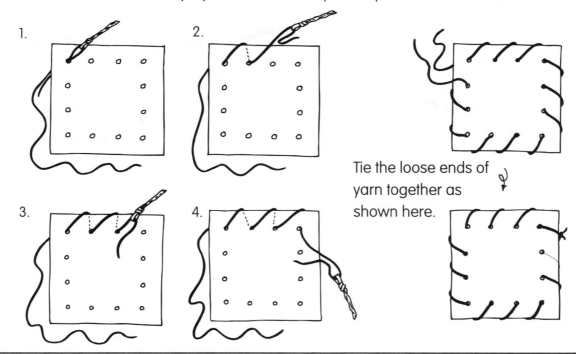

Tie the loose ends of yarn together as shown here.

Cut-ups Supplies Checklist

lacing card patterns	crayons	bottle caps
yarn	markers	sand
ribbon	glitter	seashells
twine	glitter pens	pipe cleaners
shoelaces	wiggle eyes	paper clips
hole punches	cut-out alphabet letters	paint
scissors	sticky dots	paintbrushes
buttons	construction paper	glue
pom poms	cotton balls	twist ties
pasta noodles (uncooked)	sequins	brown grocery bags
artificial flowers	beads	_____
star stickers	cotton swabs	_____
rice (uncooked)	craft sticks	_____

Acorn

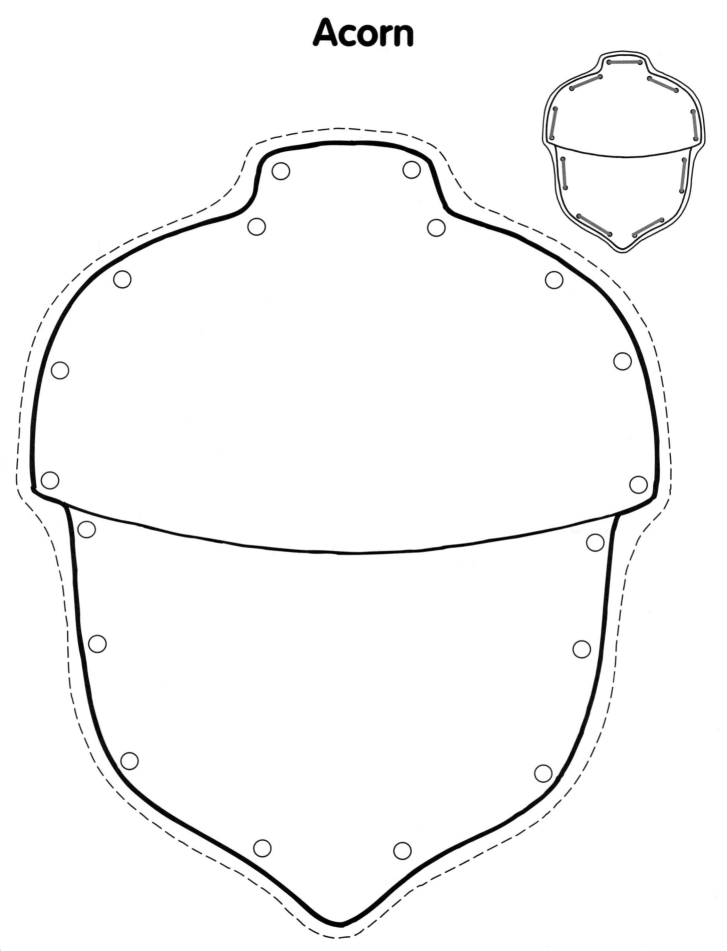

Alligator

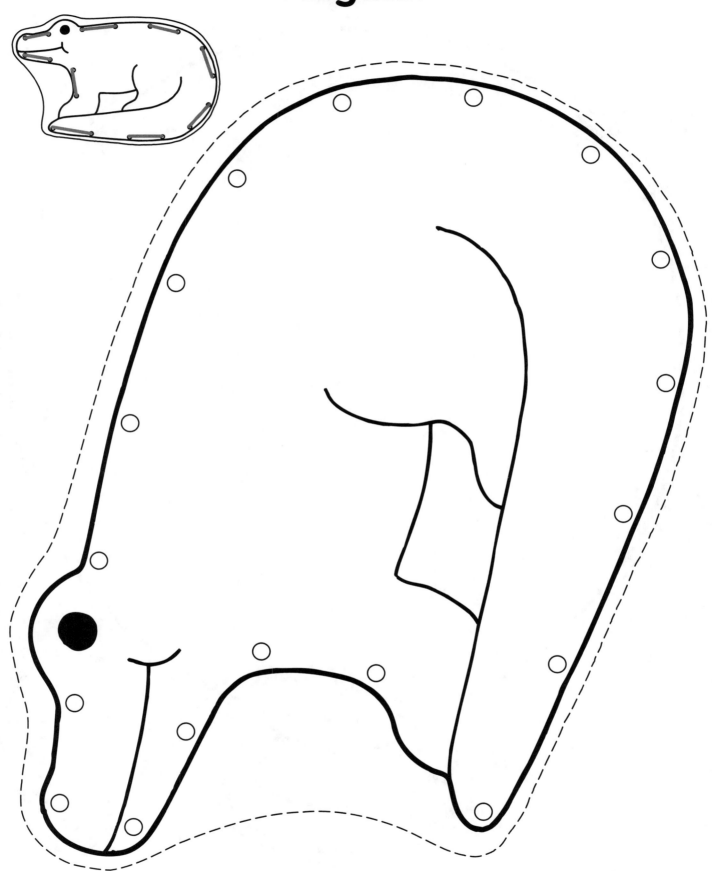

Balloon

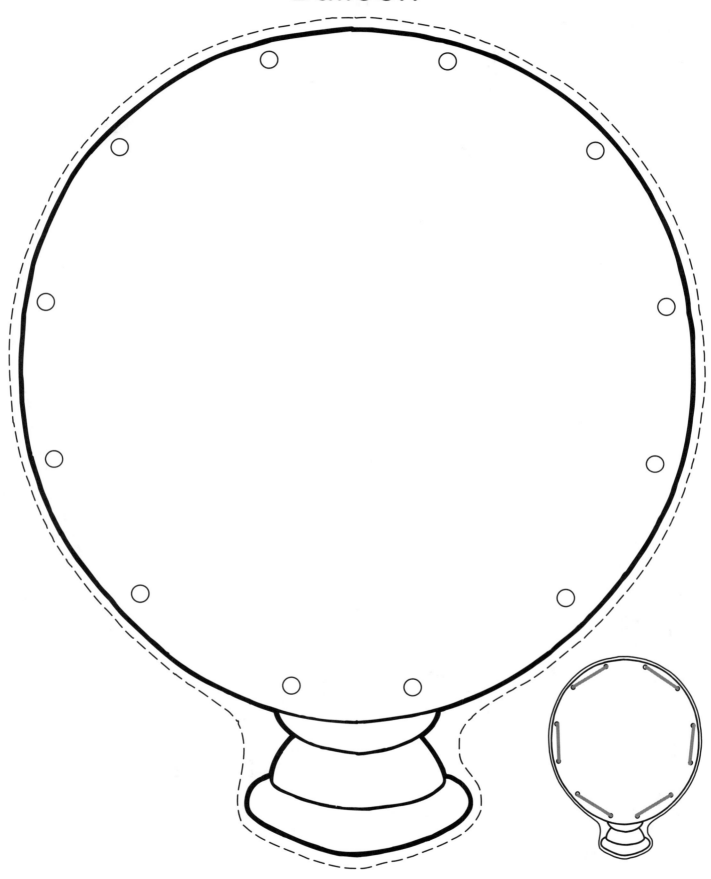

Bear

Cake

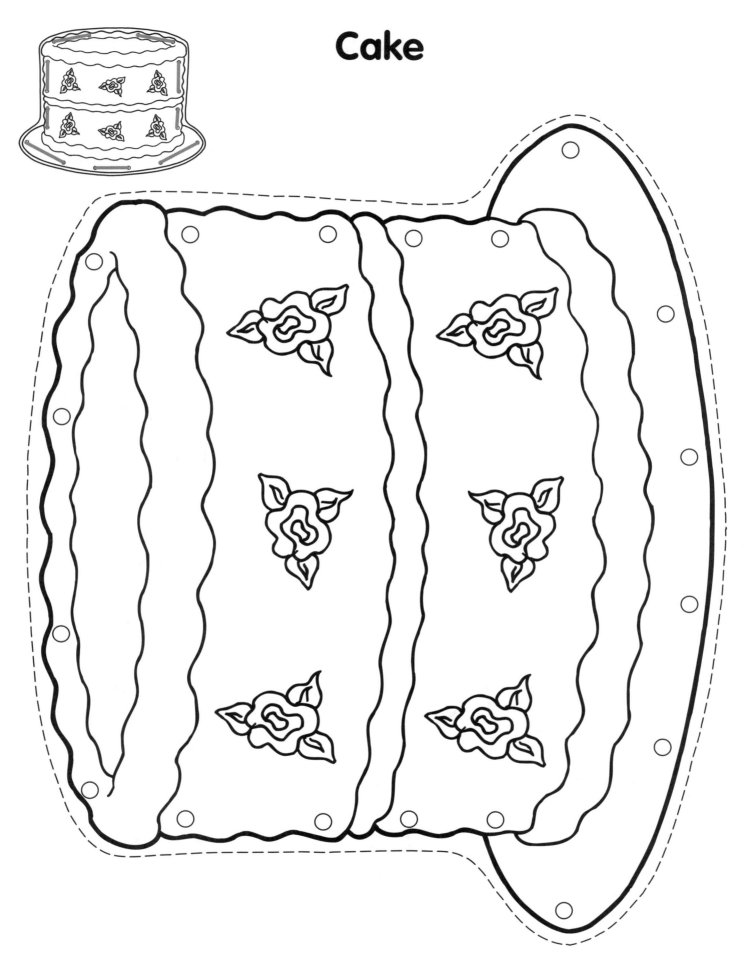

Cat

Drum

Duck

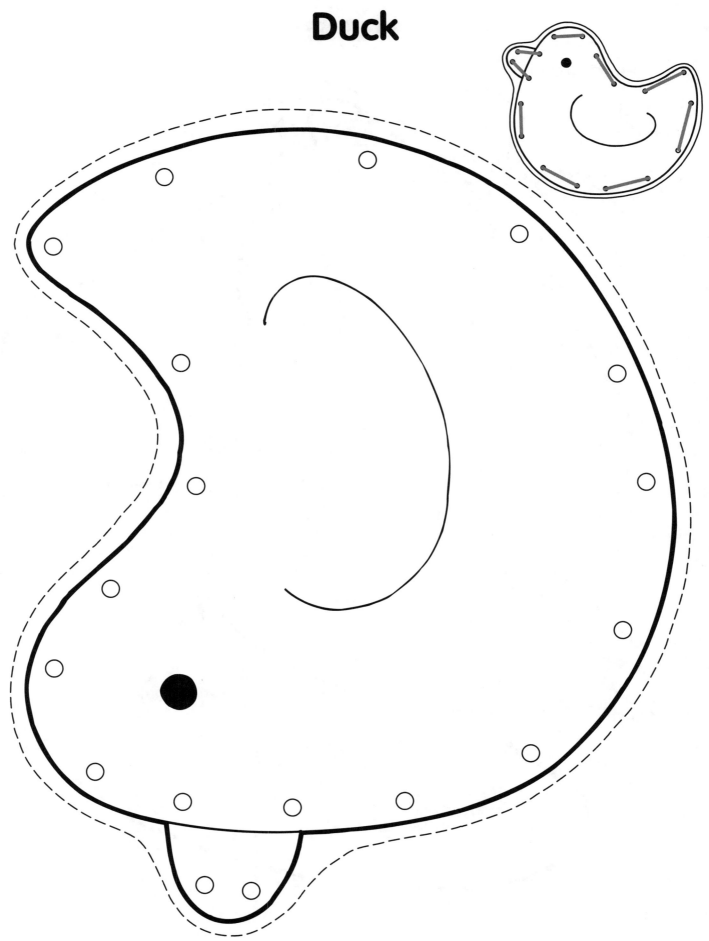

Eagle

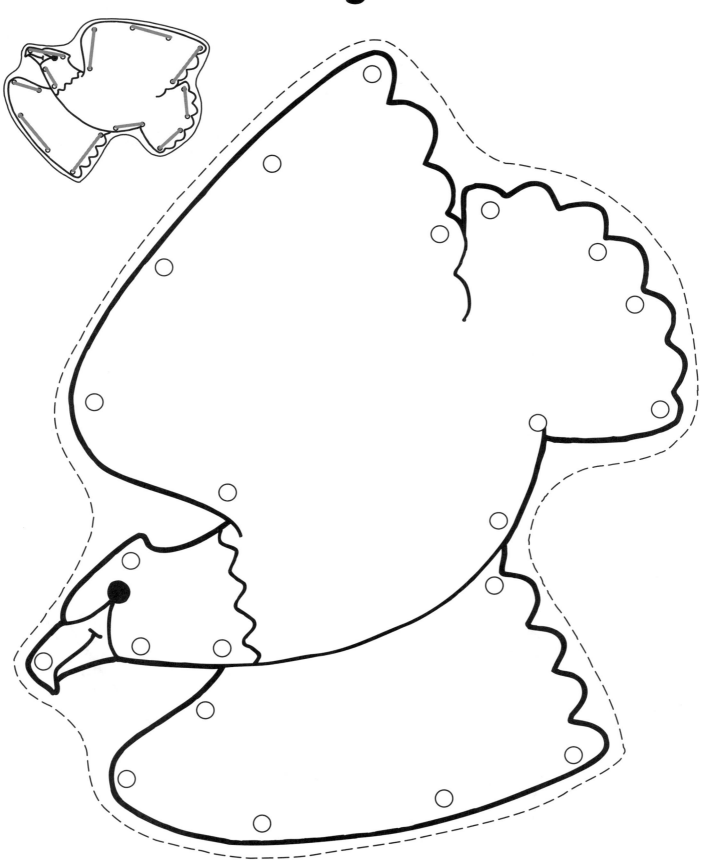

Egg

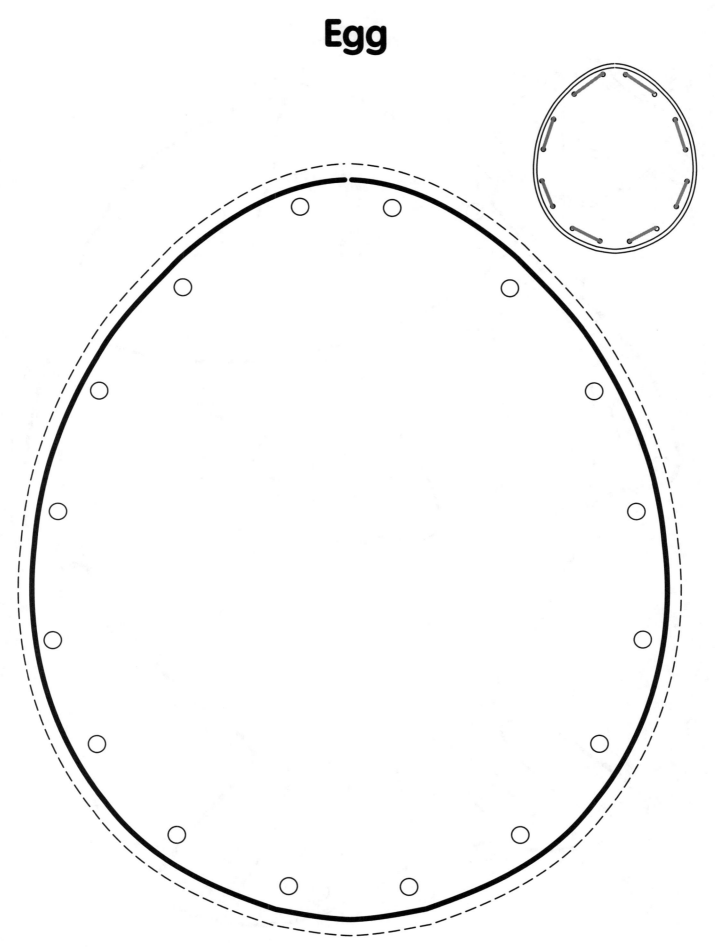

Fish

Flower

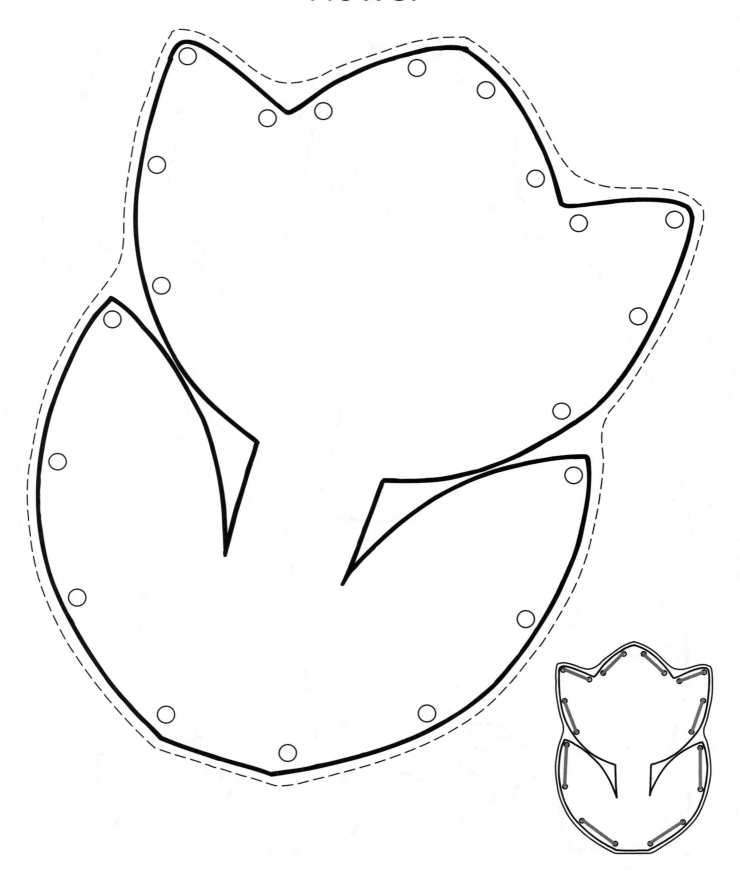

Gorilla

Grapes

Heart

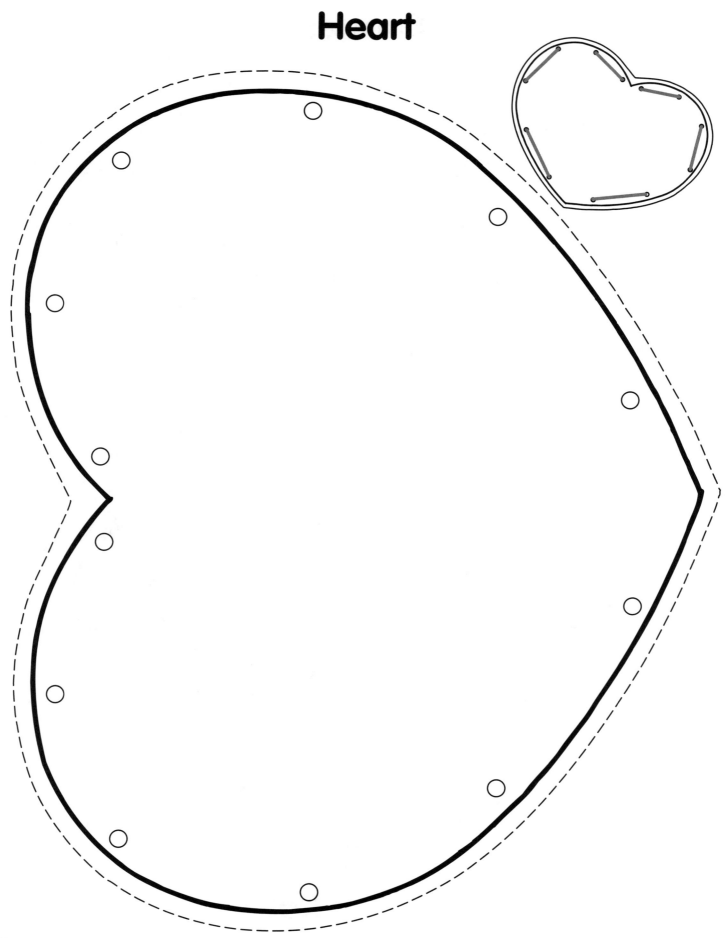

Hippopotamus

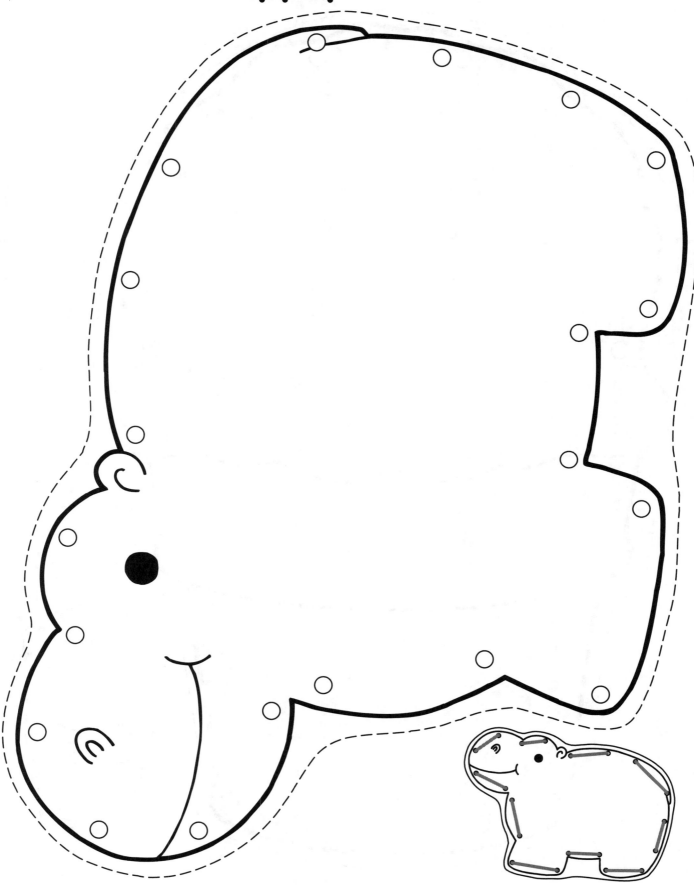

Ice Cream

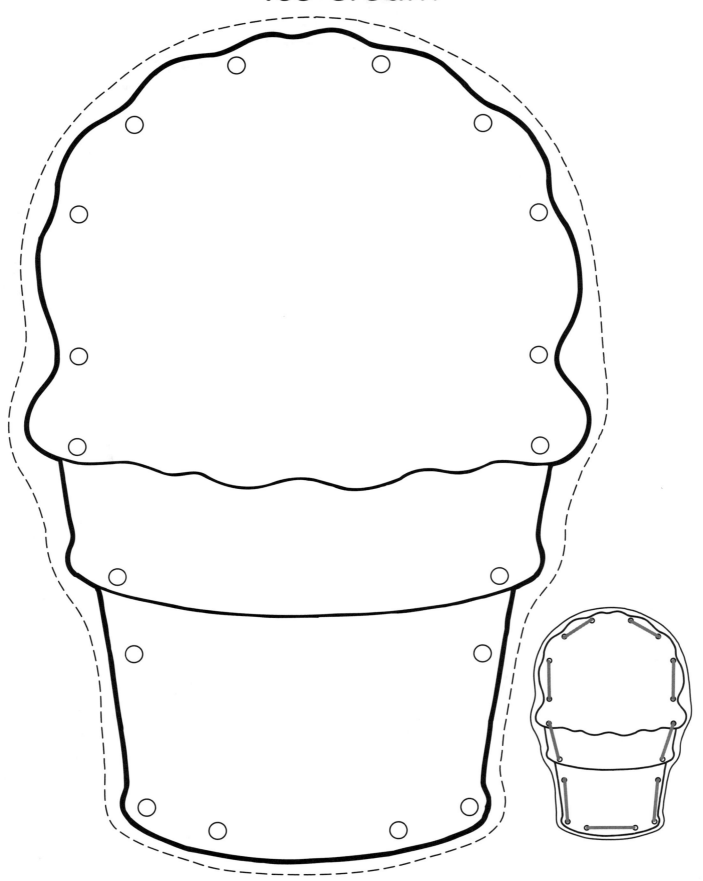

Igloo

Jar

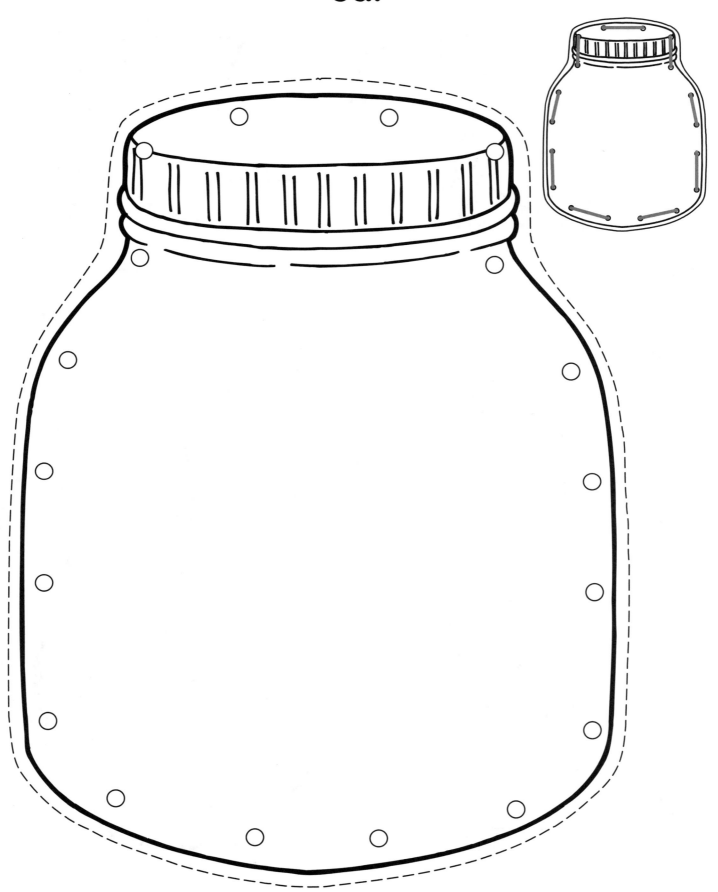

Jellyfish

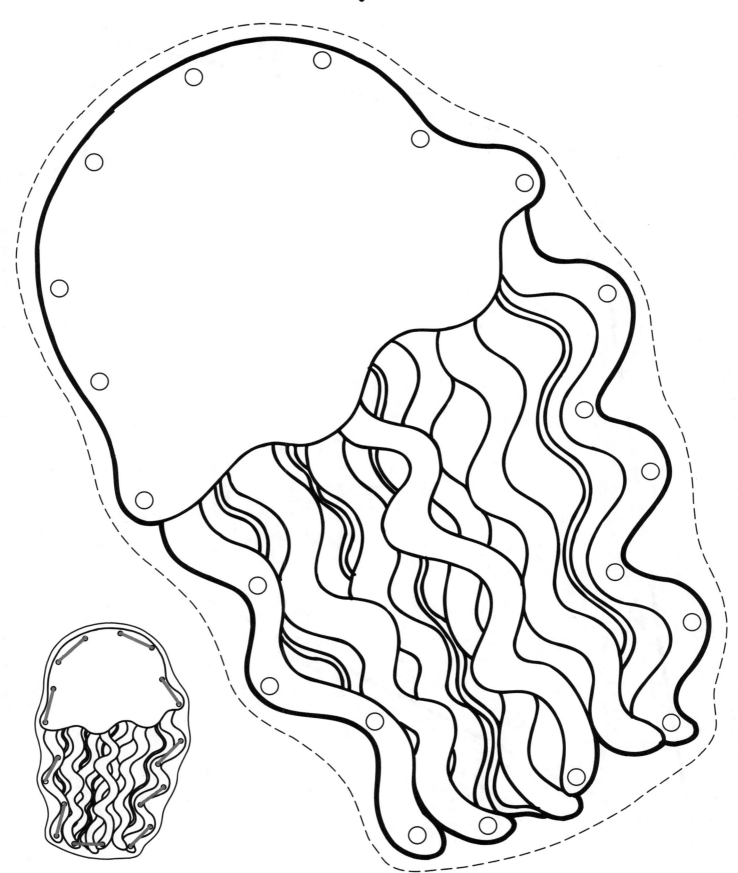

Kite

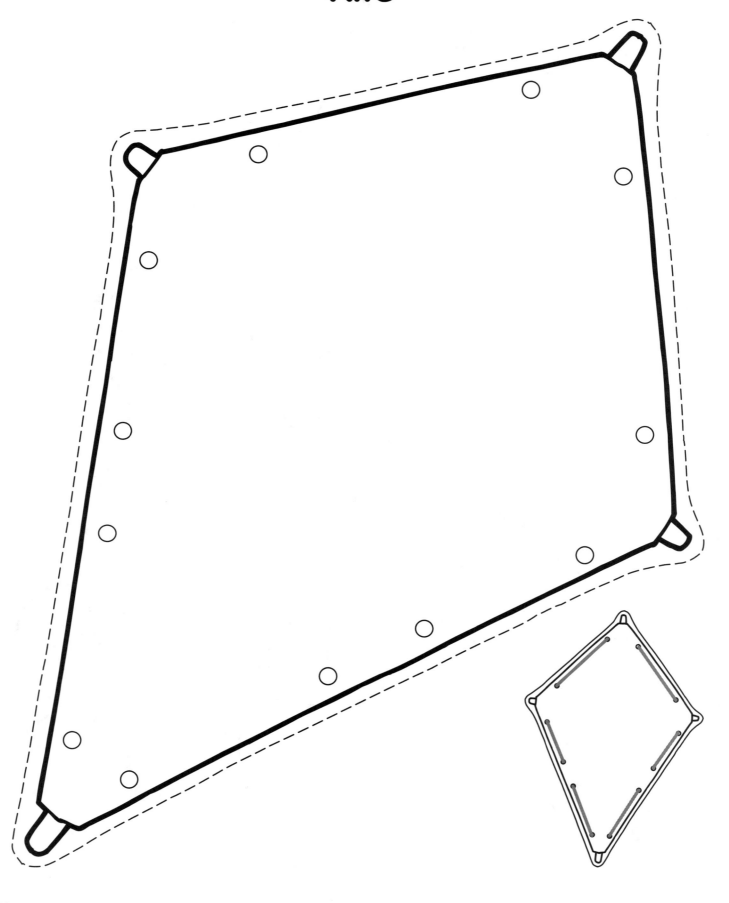

Koala

Ladybug

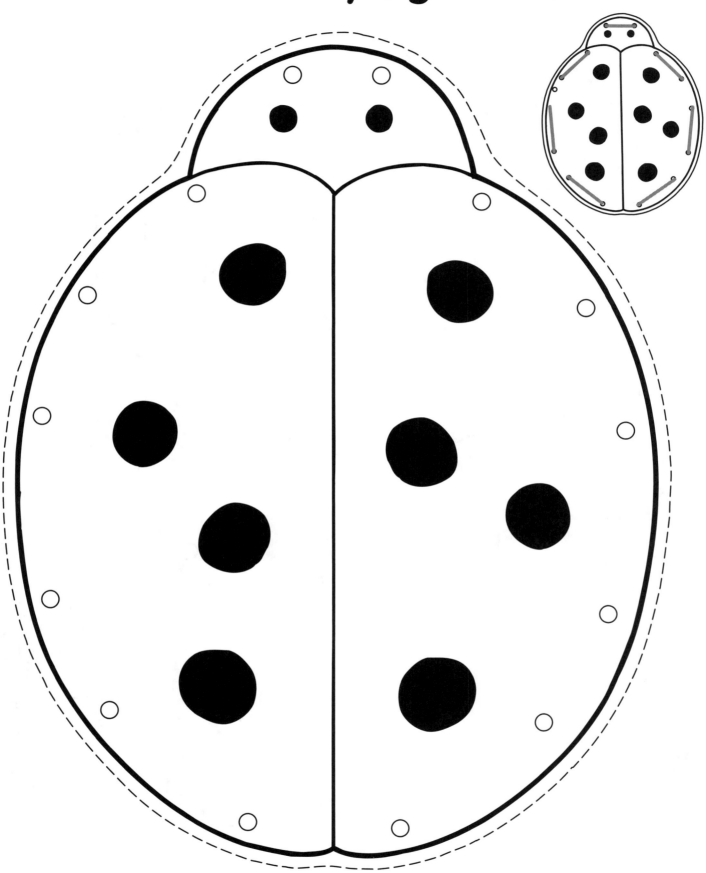

Lunch Box

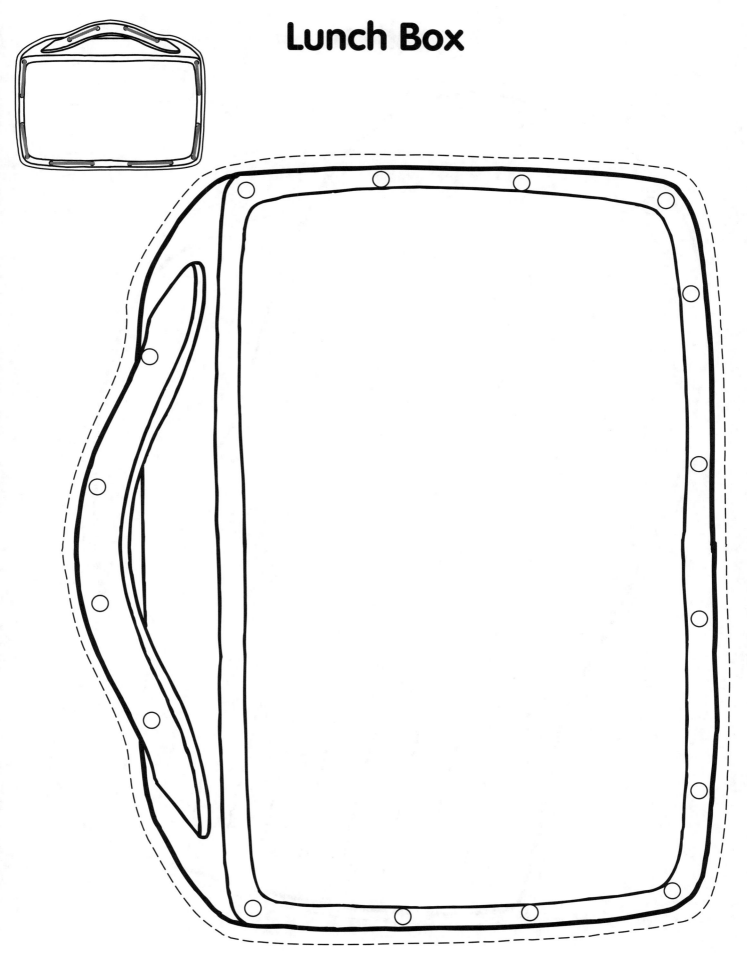

Mitten

Mouse

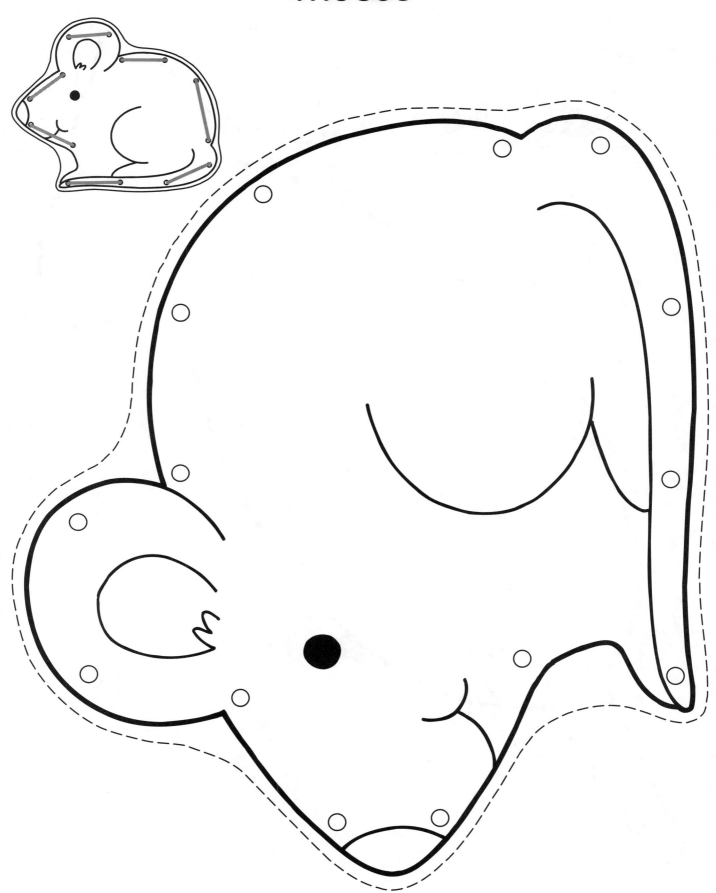

Narwhal

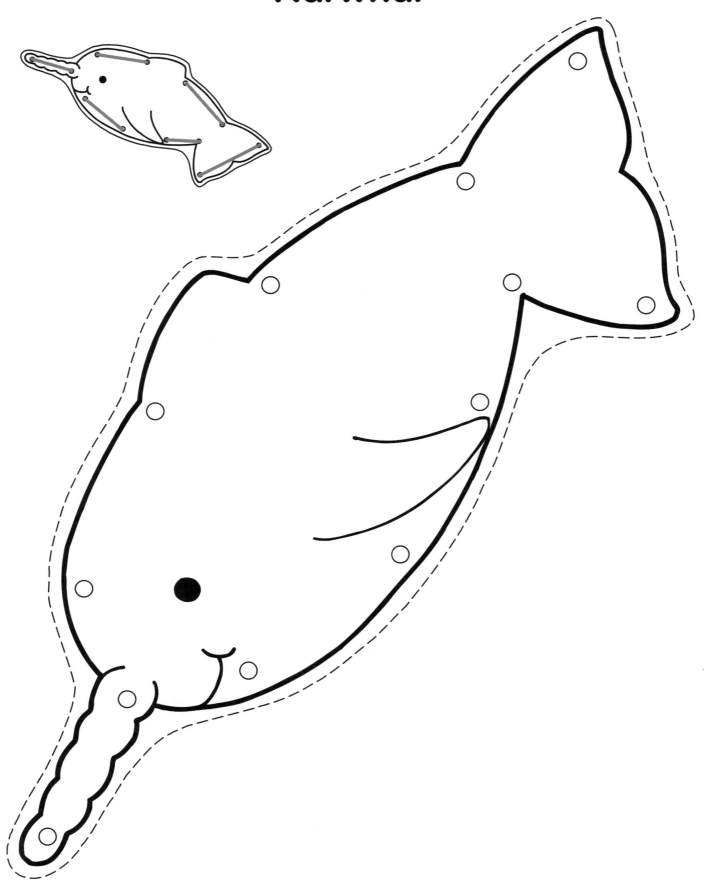

Nest

Overalls

Owl

Pig

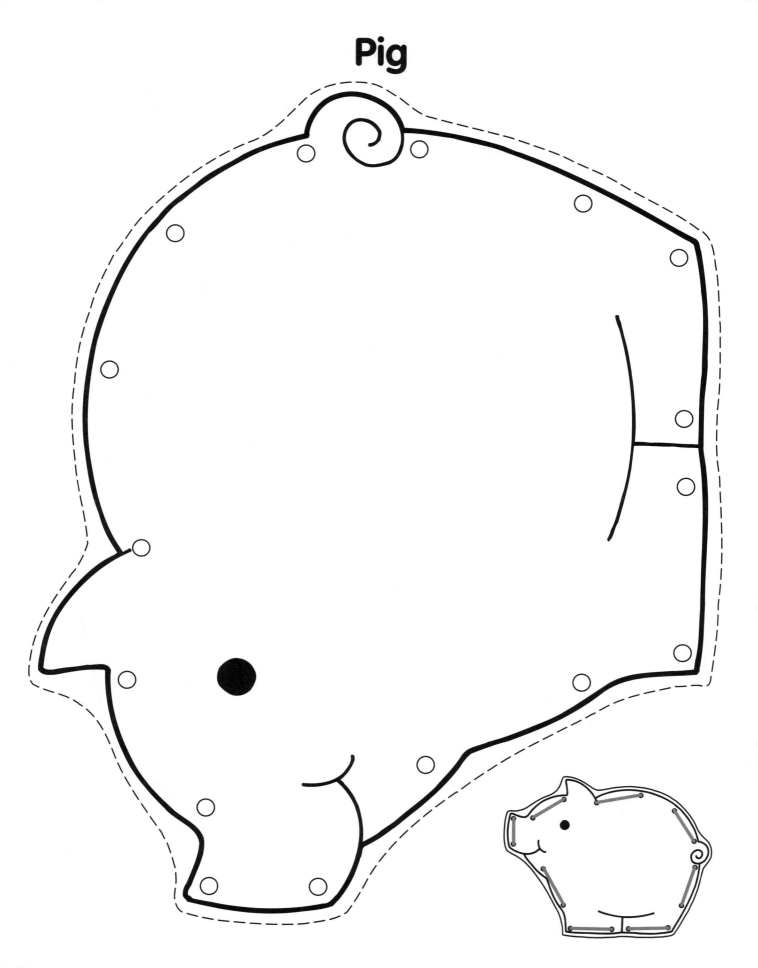

Present

Quail

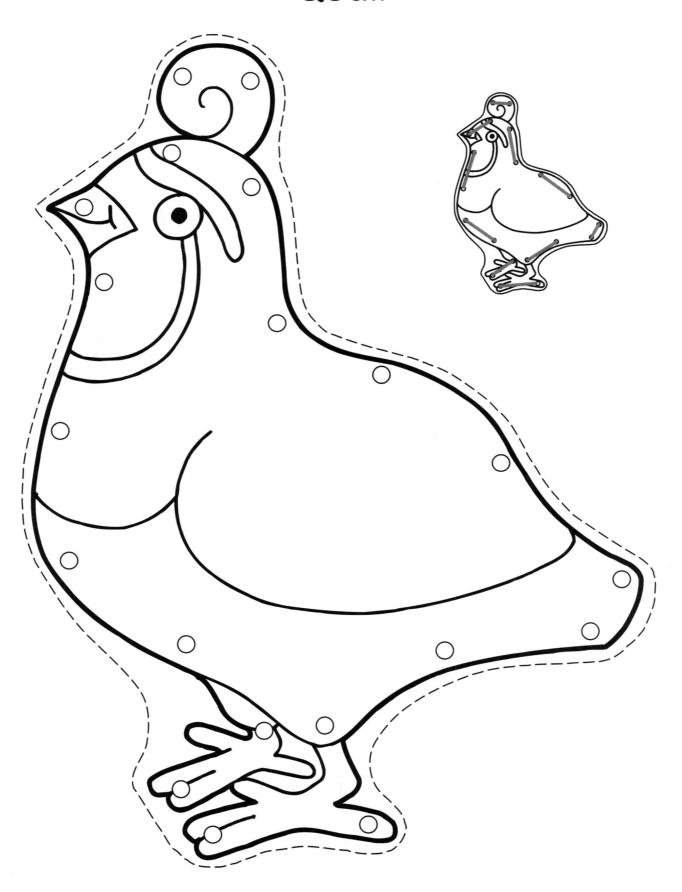

Quilt

Rabbit

Robot

Shell

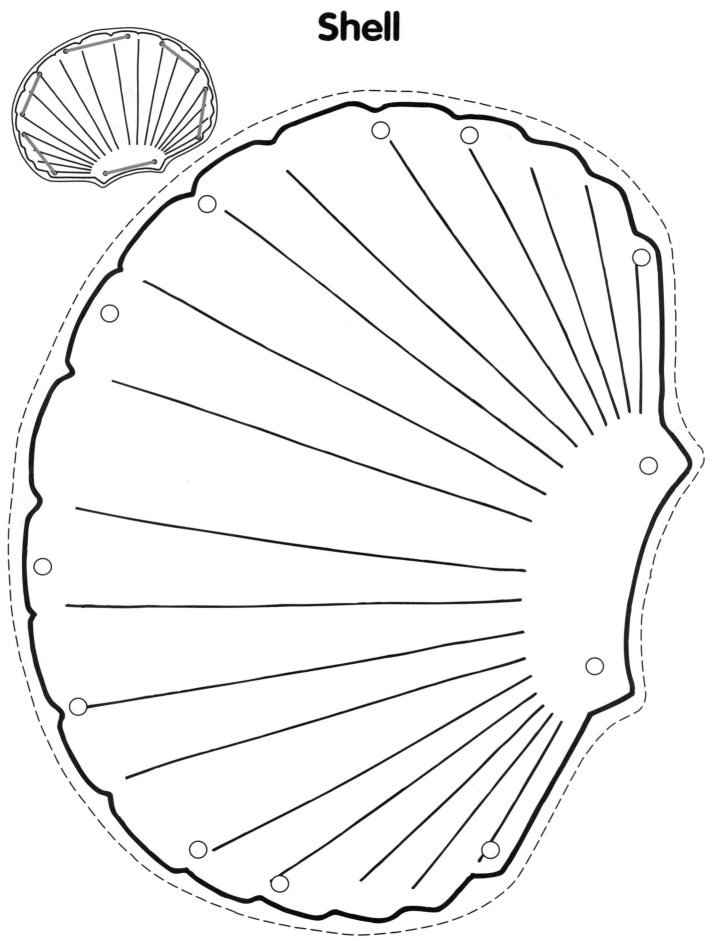

Snail

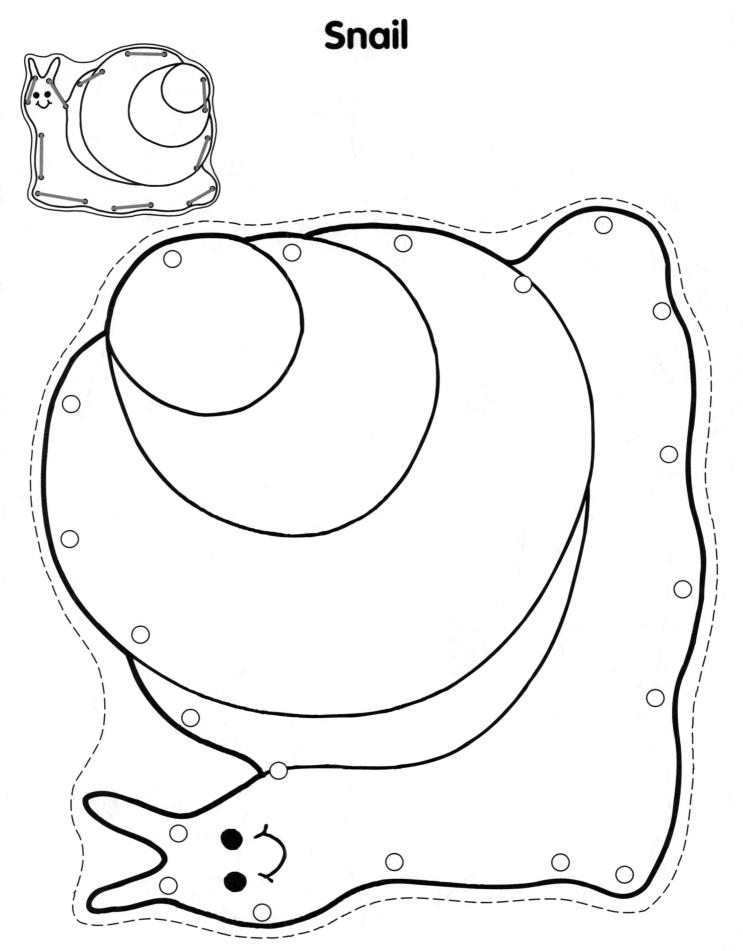

Tiger

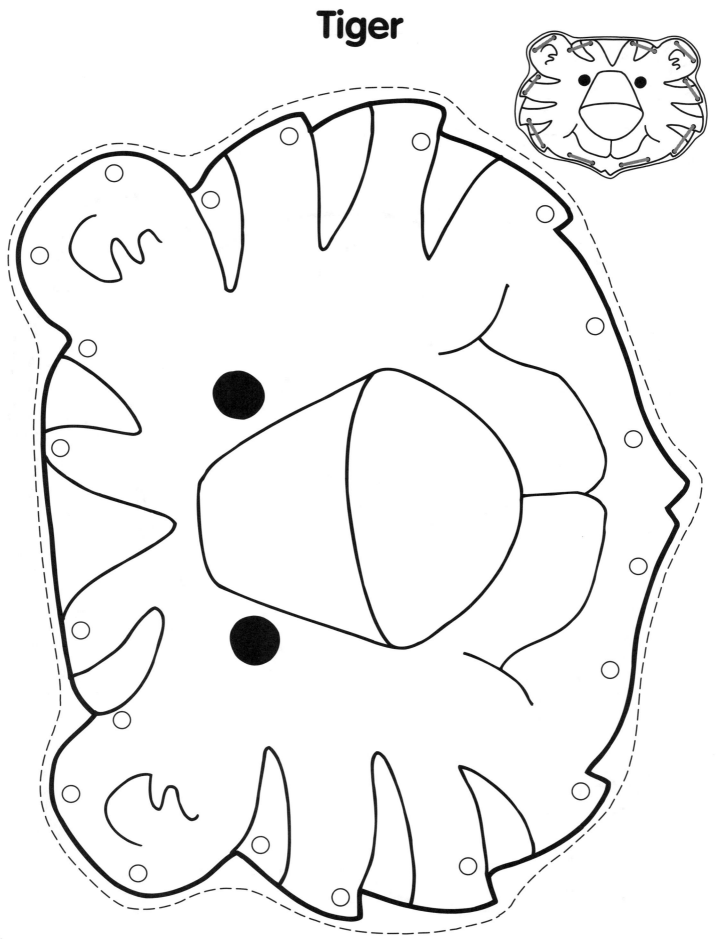

Tree

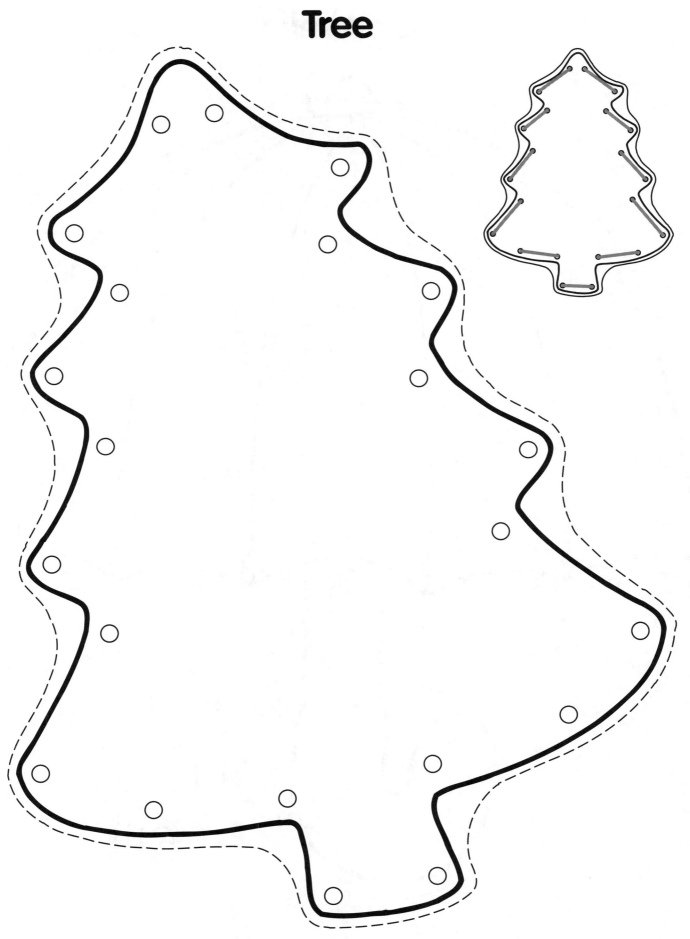

Umbrella

Unicorn

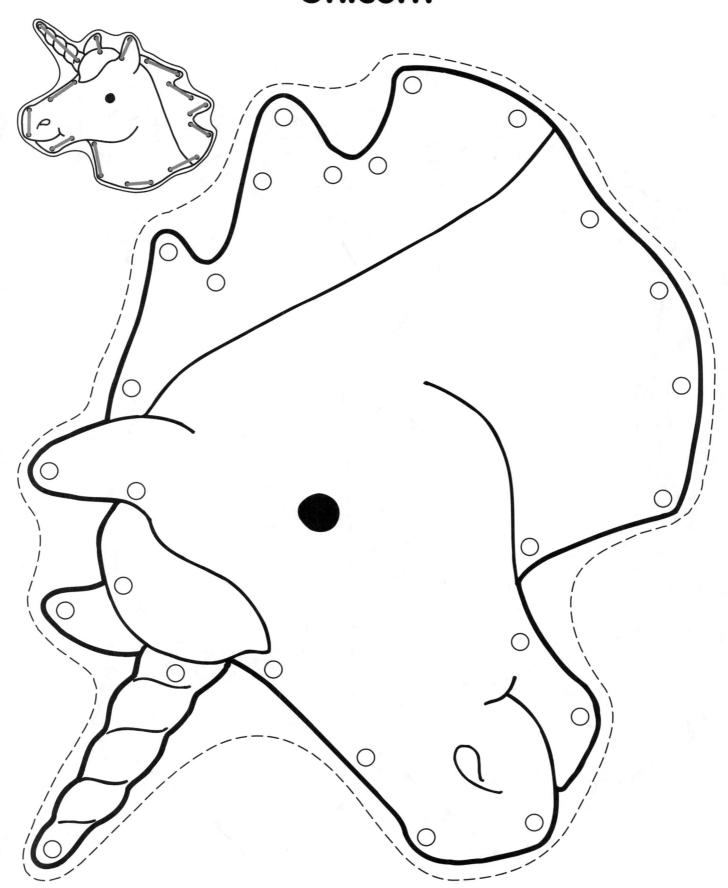

Vest

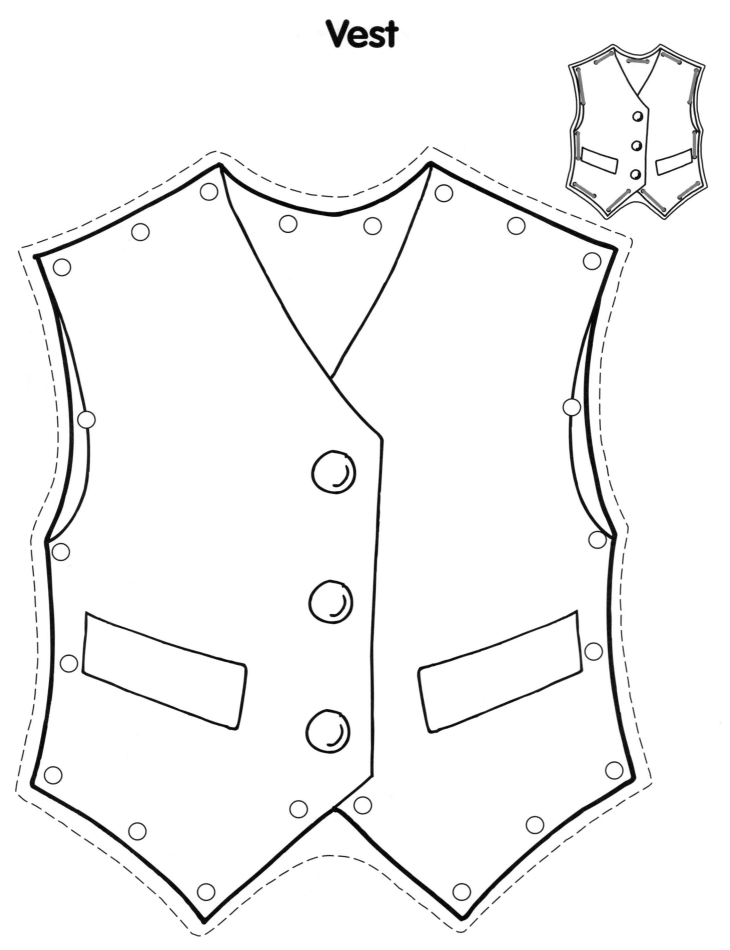

Vulture

Watch

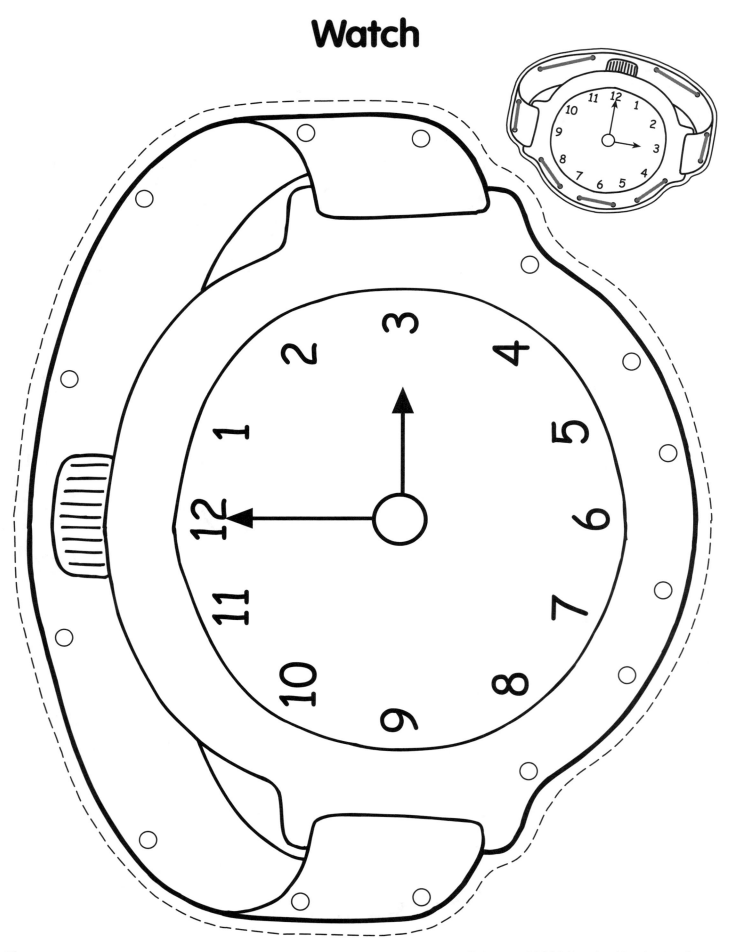

Whale

Letter X

Xylophone

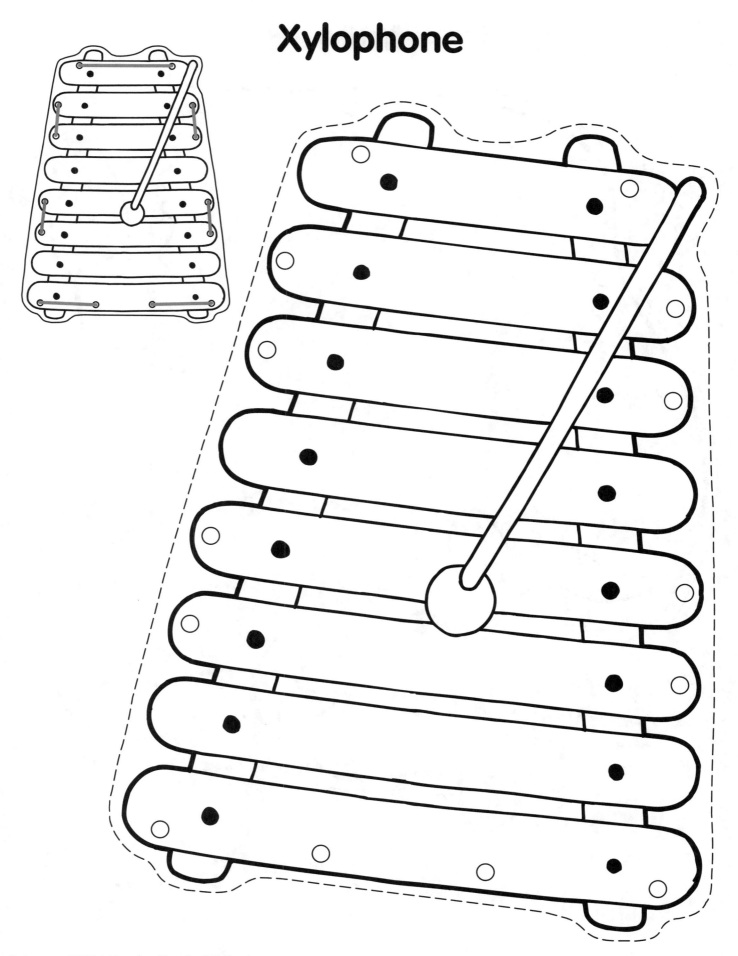

Yak

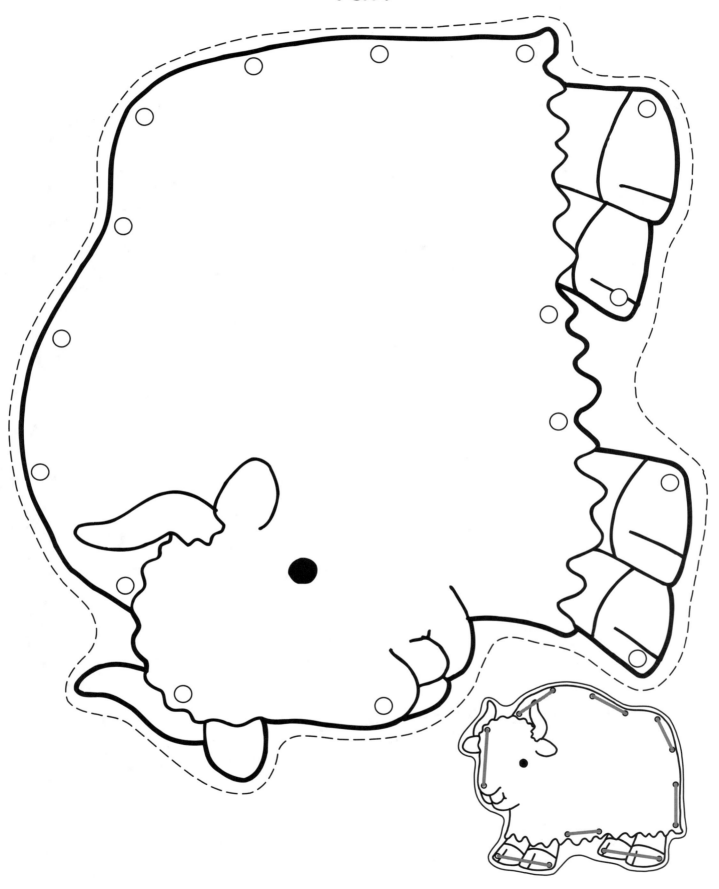

Yarn

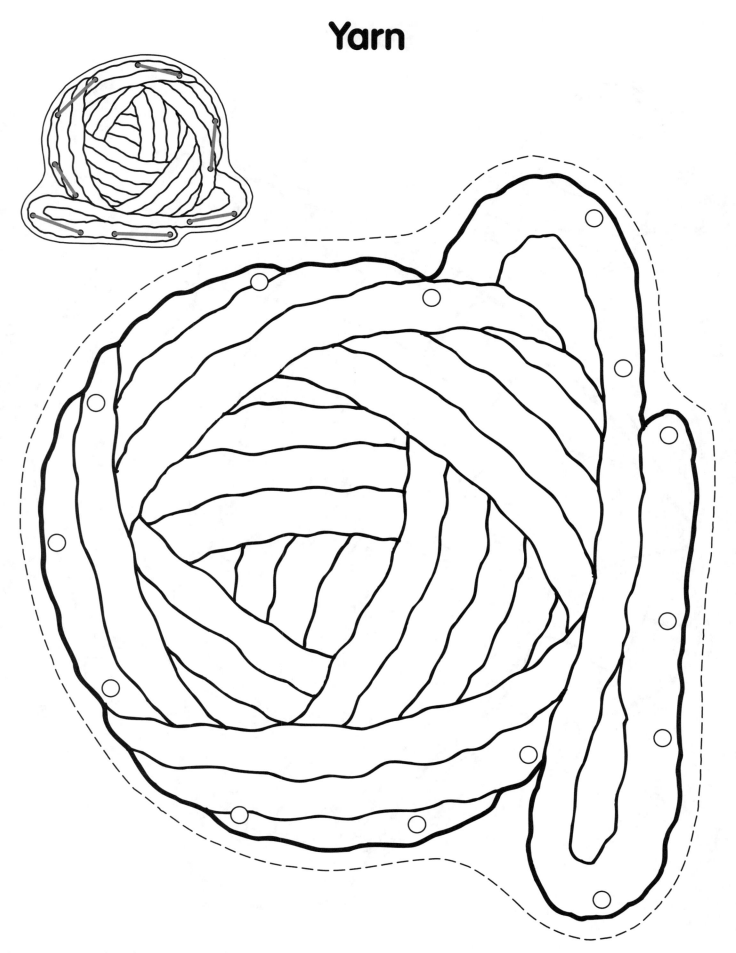

Zebra

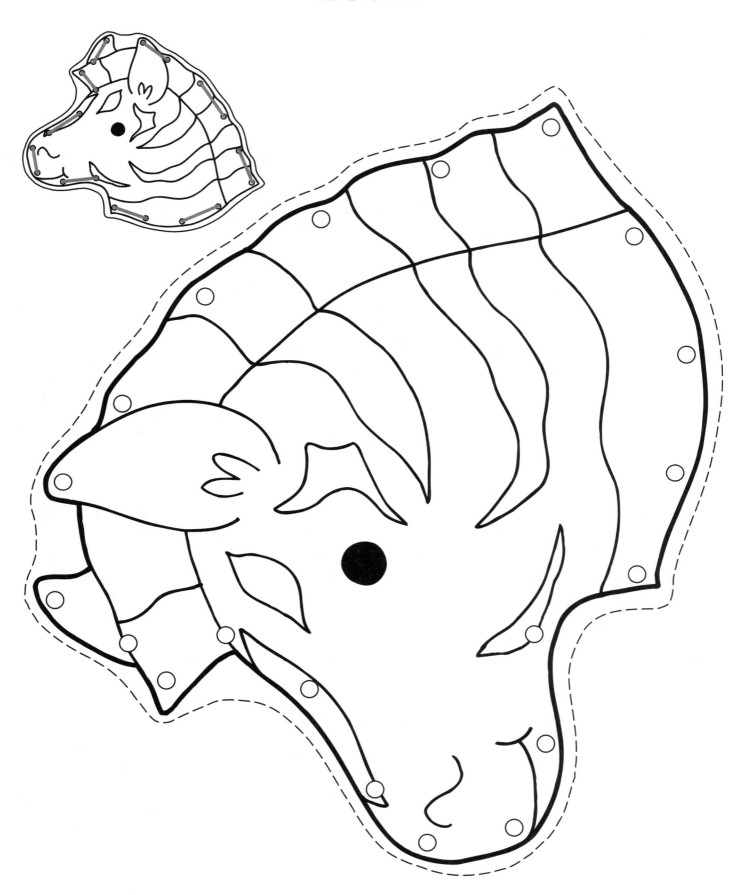

Zipper

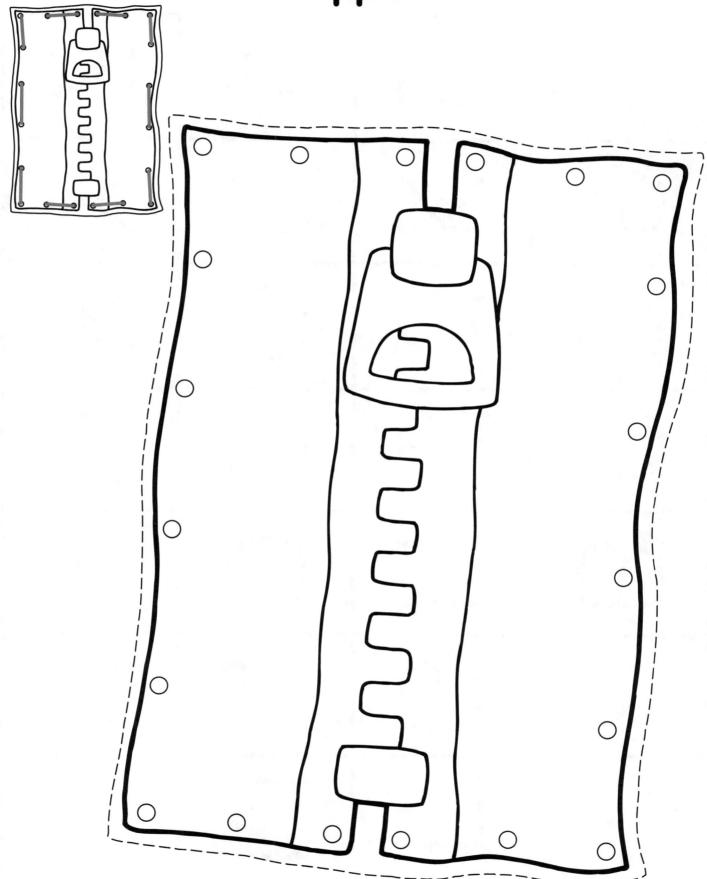

Letter Cards

	L	S	Z
E	K	R	Y
D	J	Q	X
C	I	P	W
B	H	O	V
A	G	N	U
	F	M	T

Letter Cards

	l	s	z
e	k	r	y
d	j	q	x
c	i	p	w
b	h	o	v
a	g	n	u
	f	m	t

Textured Cut-ups

Provide children with a variety of craft materials to make decorative Textured Cut-ups for classroom or home display.

Materials:

Cut-ups patterns	scissors	crayons or markers
hole punch	yarn	buttons
pom poms	glitter	sand
pasta noodles (uncooked)	sequins	beads
rice (uncooked)	glue	

Prepare a worktable with a basket filled with oak tag Cut-ups patterns and small containers filled with craft materials. Have children wear aprons to protect their clothing. Have children color, cut out, and punch holes, around their Cut-ups patterns to form lacing cards. Demonstrate how to straight or loop lace yarn through the holes around a lacing card as shown on pages 6 and 7. Then help each child lace his or her lacing card and tie the loose ends of yarn together. Show how to apply glue and attach craft materials to a lacing card. Encourage children to decorate their lacing cards with one or more of the craft materials listed above. Display finished Textured Cut-ups on walls, windows, and doors.

Cut-ups Vest

Provide children with brown grocery bags and Cut-ups to make vests to wear during an I Know My ABCs sing-a-long.

Materials:

Cut-ups patterns	brown grocery bags	scissors	crayons or markers
hole punch	yarn	glue	

Each child will need a brown grocery bag and a Cut-ups pattern. Have children color, cut out and punch holes around each of their Cut-ups patterns to form lacing cards. Show how to make and thread yarn through a twist-tie needle (see page 6). Demonstrate how to straight lace or loop lace yarn through the holes around a lacing card as shown on pages 6 and 7. Have children lace each of their lacing cards, then help children tie the loose ends of yarn together.

Recruit parent volunteers to help children make vests from brown grocery bags. Cut a slit along the center of one of the wide panels of a brown grocery bag. Cut two arm holes and a neckline. Have each child glue his or her finished lacing card to the back of his of her vest. Use a marker to write the matching upper and lower-case letters on the front of each child's Cut-ups Vest.

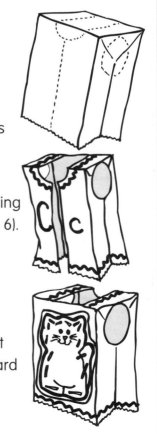

Cut-ups Quilt

Cut-ups quilts make colorful wall and bulletin board displays.

Materials:

Cut-ups patterns	scissors	crayons or markers
hole punch	yarn	twist ties
colored construction paper	glue	

Reproduce and provide each child with an oak tag Cut-ups pattern. Have children color, cut out, and punch holes around each of their Cut-ups patterns to form lacing cards. Show how to make and thread yarn through a twist-tie needle (see page 6). Demonstrate how to straight lace or loop lace yarn through the holes around a lacing card as shown on pages 6 and 7. Have children lace each of their lacing cards, then help children tie the loose ends of yarn together.

Measure and cut colored construction paper squares large enough to fit one lacing card on each square with an ample margin. Glue each child's finished lacing card onto a sheet of colored construction paper to form a quilt square. Punch an even number of holes along all four sides of each quilt square. Use yarn to lace squares together to form an alphabet Cut-ups Quilt.

Stuffed Alphabet Pillows

Decorate your alphabet skills practice center with hanging alphabet pillows.

Materials:

Cut-ups patterns	Letter cards	scissors
crayons or markers	hole punch	yarn
twist ties	glue	plastic grocery bags

Provide each child with two identical Cut-ups patterns. Have children color only one, then cut out both patterns. Provide matching letter cards (pp. 60-61) for children to glue one to the front of the colored Cut-up and one to the back of the uncolored Cut-up. Help each child stack (colored Cut-up on top) and punch holes around the Cut-ups. Demonstrate how to straight lace or loop lace yarn through the holes around a lacing card as shown on pages 6 and 7. Help each child lace yarn through both lacing cards to form a pillow. **Do not** lace yarn through the last four holes. Have children stuff Cut-ups pillow forms with plastic grocery bags. Then help each child finish lacing and tying the loose ends of yarn together.

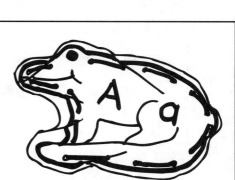

Request For Craft Supplies

Dear Parent,

Please send supplies listed below to school with your child for our alphabet practice workstation.

☐ yarn	☐ rice (uncooked)	☐ cotton swabs
☐ ribbon	☐ glitter	☐ craft sticks
☐ twine	☐ glitter pens	☐ bottle caps
☐ shoelaces	☐ wiggle eyes	☐ sand
☐ buttons	☐ sticky dots	☐ seashells
☐ pom poms	☐ cotton balls	☐ pipe cleaners
☐ pasta noodles (uncooked)	☐ sequins	☐ paper clips
☐ artificial flowers	☐ beads	

Thank you,

_____

Teacher